# I Want to Age Like That!

## A Companion Guide Workbook

Diana L. Bitner, MD, NCMP

# I Want to Age Like That!

## A Companion Guide Workbook

ISBN 978-1-939294-71-5

WOMEN'S HEALTH

www.truewomenshealth.com

Published by

# Table of Contents

# I Want to Age Like That! Workbook

"This workbook will guide you on a journey of deliberate wellbeing. In order to age as you choose, careful planning and execution is required. Use expert knowledge and experience to reconnect to your goals and work through daily challenges. Welcome to the W*A*I*Pointes® way of thinking!"


-Diana Bitner, MD, NCMP, author of *I Want to Age Like That!*

# Chapter One

## *This is Not My Mother's Menopause*

I remember getting chills when reading Christiane Northrup's book, "The Wisdom of Menopause," about her leading women to meditate and feel back to generations of women who went before and to honor the unspoken connections that exist. The image is very powerful. I have gratitude for women who came before me and created a foundation of experience and wisdom.

Women no longer have to suffer through midlife and menopause like our female ancestors. We have the power of knowledge, experience, and modern medical options. Our actions will guide our daughters and granddaughters.

To do the first exercise in this workbook, think about the women in your life and in your history, such as your mother, grandmother, and great grandmother. When you think about them, what do you feel? What do you remember? Were they matriarchs running the household? Were they meek and not powerful, or did they express and own their power? Were they loud or quiet, healthy or not so healthy? Did they break or follow rules? Name them and describe your memory of them.

Many women do not know when or how their female relatives went through "the change" or menopause. One of my patients remembered that every time she would visit her mom, her mother would leave the room saying, "You don't love me; all my children hate me!" Her dad would say, "Don't mind her, it's the menopause." Her mother would later apologize. After several years of this same behavior, her mother finally acted like herself again. My patient did NOT want to act or feel the same way.

What are your memories? Write them in the space provided below.

Great Grandmothers:

_____

_____

_____

_____

Grandmothers:

_____

_____

_____

Aunts/Great Aunts:

_____

_____

_____

Mother:

_____

_____

_____

Sisters:

_____

_____

_____

_____

**What is your family medical history?** Think about which of your ancestors had medical problems, and for those who have died, what was their cause of death? In addition, check with other family members to be sure you don't miss any possible medical problems. Write your answers below, specifically looking at diabetes, cancers, heart issues, osteoporosis, obesity, and emotional issues such as suicide.

There might be missing information, but complete it to the best of your ability. We will refer to it frequently in W*A*I*Pointes® planning.

Great Grandparents:

Grandparents:

Parents:

Aunts/Uncles:

_____

_____

Siblings:

_____

_____

_____

_____

When you are finished listing your family members and their respective medical issues, take a few moments to consider what you are worried about. In the W*A*I*Pointes® process, you will be asked to focus on what you want to happen; however, pause here to consider what you want NOT to happen. What scares you about aging and menopause? What disease (such as diabetes or breast cancer) do you NOT want?

Write your answers in the space provided below.

Undesired Outcomes:

_____

_____

_____

_____

Now, turn it around to the positive. As you think about aging, your future, and your future health, how do you WANT to age? It will not be as hard as you think to achieve your goals. Just because your ancestors had cancer or diabetes or obesity does not mean you have to deal with those same issues. It is possible to have more of what you want.

Write them in the space provided below.

Desired outcomes for future health:

_____

_____

_____

_____

# Chapter Two

## *Surviving Midlife When Good Hormones Go Bad*

It is hard to deal with body changes when you do not understand what is happening. The most common complaints of women coming into a midlife and menopause health clinic include the following:

- I do not feel like myself.

- My periods are changing. Why?

- I am anxious and feel a sense of dread, but my life is good. Why?

- Why am I gaining weight?

- Why do I feel worried all the time?

- Why is my sex drive low? I used to love sex! And why does it hurt?

I have learned my job as a physician does not start with fixing the problem—it starts with answering the question, "Why?"

As we explore why symptoms are happening, it is important to determine your current stage of life—peri- or menopause—in order to understand if the symptoms are related to hormone imbalance. By knowing your stage, you will then have a better idea of what to expect.

To do so, we start with a flowchart derived from the STRAW Workshop (next page), which was last updated in 2011. It is a consensus agreement on which terms to use to describe the changes in life for women. *Menopause 2011 The Journal of The North American Menopause Society, Vol. 19, No. 4.*

To begin, write your answers in the spaces provided below.

If you have NOT had a hysterectomy:

- What was the date of your last menstrual period? _____

- When was the first time your period was different by more than seven days (early or late)?_____

- When was the first time you went 60 days without a period? _____

- When is the first month you had symptoms such as night sweats, increased PMS-mood changes, or a marked increase in body complaints, like menstrual migraines, during the week before your period? _____

## HORMONE PHASE FLOWCHART

If you have had a hysterectomy and still have your ovaries, your stage can be determined using symptoms and a blood test called FSH. FSH stands for Follicle Stimulating Hormone, and if it is high, that indicates your ovaries are not making as much estrogen or any at all. If your periods stop due to chemotherapy or you have had your ovaries surgically removed, this is also menopause. Induced menopause can be especially difficult because the changes are so abrupt.

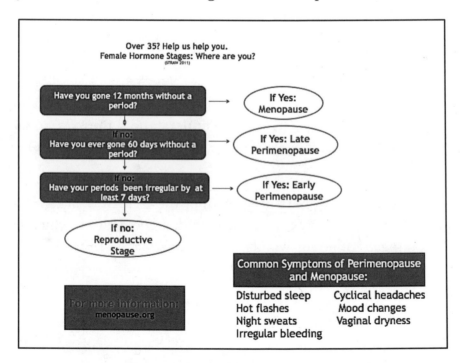

What is your current stage of ovarian function? _____

The most common symptoms of the menopause transition are listed below. Each symptom has many causes, some listed in the table below. For example, hot flashes are caused by more than low estrogen, and taking hormone medication is not the only solution to reduce hot flashes. The table describes some common symptoms and factors that can be at play for symptom frequency and intensity.

**Possible Menopause Symptoms/Causes**

| Menopause Symptoms | Possible Causes |
|---|---|
| Hot flashes/night sweats | Low estrogen, low water intake, sugar rush, alcohol, sleep deprivation, stress adrenalin rush, low brain chemicals, i.e. serotonin |
| Difficulty controlling weight | Inadequate activity, excess calories, insulin resistance, sleep deprivation |
| Low energy | Sleep deprivation, high sugar intake, low water intake, inadequate exercise, depression or anxiety |
| Lower libido | Poor self-image, relationship troubles, depression or anxiety, sleep deprivation, stress, low estrogen and testosterone |
| Mood change, anxiety or depression | Sleep deprivation, low brain chemicals, i.e. serotonin, low estrogen, increased stress points |
| Vaginal dryness, bladder urgency | Low estrogen, frequent vaginal infection, low libido (dryness at penetration if not wanting), bladder infection, interstitial cystitis |
| Heavy or irregular periods | High estrogen with low progesterone |

In the last two weeks, how many of these symptoms have you experienced? List YOUR symptoms and include possible causes and/or triggers from the chart above.

| Menopause Symptoms | Yes/No | How Many in 24 Hours? | Possible Causes/Triggers |
|---|---|---|---|
| Hot flashes/night sweats | | | |
| Difficulty controlling weight | | | |
| Low energy | | | |
| Lower libido | | | |
| Mood change, anxiety or depression | | | |
| Vaginal dryness, bladder urgency | | | |
| Heavy or irregular periods | | | |

Knowing why you have your symptoms is the first step to feeling better; knowledge is power. The next step is to consider lifestyle habits that can trigger the symptoms, even if you choose to take medication. It can also be helpful to track the symptom frequency and severity for a bit to help confirm the symptoms are getting better. I recommend you track your symptoms over the next two weeks and then move forward in the workbook, and/or take your list of symptoms to your certified menopause provider, whom you can find at menopause.org, to discuss treatment options.

# Chapter Three

## *Owning My Own Power: W\*A\*I\*Pointes®*

W\*A\*I\*Pointes® is built on the concept of helping you define your personal truth and desired level of wellness in the future. What is wellness? It is the result of deliberate planning and subsequent actions that lead to you having the happiness and wellbeing of your dreams. To achieve wellness, we have to start with the basics, which is to fully describe your future goals that we group into nine W\*A\*I\*Pointes® categories. WAI stands for "Who Am I" and is an evidence-based curriculum using personalized goal-setting for specific health outcomes. Many conditions of aging are preventable, but planning is required. Just as a financial planner would ask you to commit to financial goals for retirement, W\*A\*I\*Pointes® will ask you to commit to healthcare goals.

The *I Want to Age Like That!* book explains the concept in more detail, and is to be used with this workbook. It requires some homework to walk through the process of determining your goals and plans in each of these nine categories. Everything is based on you achieving your desired level of awareness in time for a milestone event, such as your child's graduation, a retirement, a vacation or your child's wedding. The first step will be to imagine how you want to be at that event. The following is a brief explanation of W\*A\*I\*Pointes®.

### W\*A\*I\*Pointes® Nine Wellness Categories

A. <u>Ability to be Active</u>. How active do you want to be at a milestone event?

B. <u>Obesity</u>. What is your goal weight? What weight can you live with?

C. <u>Cancer</u>. Do you want cancer? If not, are you taking action to prevent getting it?

D. <u>Diabetes</u>. Are you okay with diabetes? If not, are you taking action to prevent it?

E. <u>Ease of Coping</u>. How well are you coping with the normal ups and downs of life? This will impact your health and relationships on a daily and long-term basis.

F. <u>Phase of Ovarian Function</u>. Are you in charge or are your hormones in charge?

G. <u>Good Bones</u>. How strong do you want them to be? Do you know your risk factors?

H. <u>Heart Disease</u>. What are you doing to avoid the most common cause of death in women? If you have a heart attack, do you know that you have done everything possible to avoid having one?

I. <u>Income Security</u>. What level of income security do you want to have at the milestone event? Are you financially prepared for the future? If not, what are you doing to achieve this goal?

Now that you have considered your health and wellness in these nine categories, let's get going!

# Chapter Four

## *Creating My Picture of Self (POS)*

In W*A*I*Pointes®, we will guide you in setting your health goals for a future milestone event and beyond. This is your Picture of Self (POS). Close your eyes and imagine yourself at a specific age, retirement event, or a child's graduation or wedding. Picture waking up in the morning and realizing the next phase of your life has arrived. How do you feel and look? What are you able to do? Run or walk? What are you able to afford? Do you sleep well? Do you have hot flashes? Are you happy in your relationship? Do you have heart disease, breast cancer? Are you on several medications or just vitamins? Are you confident you have done everything possible to prepare for your life events? This is about you! Today is the day to reclaim your future.

Your POS is your health goal. Whatever you write is perfect as long as you give yourself permission to think in terms of what you really want and believe that reaching your goal is possible!

What do you want? Write your answer in the spaces provided below.

_____

_____

_____

_____

_____

_____

In this chapter, you will determine your POS by category. To be able to compare your POS with your Place in Process (PIP) described in the next chapter, we need to assign your desired goals a number of 3, 2, or 1 in each category. As you read through each category, circle the level you want, and at the end of the section, write the number in the appropriate space.

## A. Ability to Be Active

How active do you want to be? What do you want to be able to do at that chosen date in the future? Look at the chart below and decide which level of activity describes where you want to be.

Which category (3, 2 or 1) best represents your goal?

### Ability to be Active POS

| 3 - Very Active<br>Presidential Fitness Score<br>>66 percentile (66%) | • More fit than 66% of women your age<br>• Moving more than 10,000 steps per day or more than 110 minutes of aerobic activity per week<br>• Strength training more than 3 times per week<br>• Only the rare barrier could derail your plans |
|---|---|
| 2 - Moderately Active<br>Presidential Fitness Score<br>>33 percentile (33%) | • More fit than 33% of women your age<br>• Moving between 5,000 and 10,000 steps per day<br>• Strength training 0-2 times per week<br>• 1-3 barriers that could derail you from your plan any day |
| 1 - Barely Active<br>Presidential Fitness Score<br><33 percentile (33%) | • Less fit than 33% of women your age<br>• Moving less than 5,000 steps per day<br>• No strength training event per week<br>• Three or more barriers to activity exist daily which disrupt your chances of activity |

My POS for Ability to Be Active is _____ (3, 2 or 1)

Why did you pick this activity goal? Write your answer in the spaces provided below.

_____

_____

_____

_____

## B. Obesity

Your weight, body fat percentage, and waist circumference determine many other health outcomes, such as risk of heart attack, stroke, diabetes, and depression or anxiety. But we all know weight is more than health risks; it can affect how we feel about ourselves, our sexuality, how likely we are to go out, our ability to exercise, how we choose the clothes we want to wear, etc. This area of wellness is not about saying that everyone needs to be skinny to be healthy, but rather determining how to reach your personal goals. If you choose to be over your ideal weight, then I would recommend you be as healthy as possible in every other area, and consider your other goals to help guide this goal. This is not to say vanity does not play a role; instead, it is about how you feel in your own skin—not based on what others think or how you might feel society dictates is the ideal weight. Commit to a realistic goal and find out in this workbook how to get it done.

**Waist Circumference** is the measurement of your waist at a line connecting your belly button to the bottom of the small of your back, above your hip bones, with your belly sucked in. Women who carry more belly fat have a higher risk of diabetes, heart attack, many cancers (including breast cancer), and stroke.

**Body Mass Index** (BMI) is a calculation based on height and weight to normalize for differences in height among women. It does not address fat distribution but can be a useful number to follow; it is used by insurance companies to calculate the risk to insure.

**Body Fat Percentage** is best measured by a special scale using a weak electric current sent through your system. It measures how long the current takes to move through your body, calculating muscle versus fat tissue. It gives a good estimate of percentage of body fat.

Which category (3, 2 or 1) best represents your goal?

## Obesity POS

| 3 - Healthy | • Waist circumference <35 inches<br>• BMI <25.0<br>• Body fat percentage in healthy range for your age (20-40: 21-33%, 41-60: 23-35%, and 61-79: 24-36%) |
|---|---|
| 2 - Overweight<br>Added health risk | • Waist circumference between 35-39 inches<br>• BMI between 25-29.9<br>• Body fat percentage in overweight range for your age (20-40: 33-39%, 41-60: 35-40%, 61-79: 36-42%) |
| 1 - Obese<br>Most health risk added | • Waist circumference 40 inches or higher<br>• BMI >30<br>• Body fat percentage obese (20-40: >39%, 41-60: >40%, 61-79: >42%) |

My POS for Obesity is _____ (3, 2 or 1)

Write your answers in the spaces provided below for your POS details.

My goal weight is: _____

Why?_____

_____

The weight I can live with is: _____

Why? _____

_____

My Body Mass Index (BMI) goal is: _____

Why?_____

_____

My waist circumference goal is: _____

Why? _____

_____

My body fat percentage goal is: _____

Why? _____

_____

## C. Cancer

The top three cancers that affect women are lung, colorectal, and breast. Uterine cancer is the fifth most common cancer in women and is very preventable, as it is related to the same risks as for heart disease. Many women have not thought of cancer as preventable and are often offended if I ask if they want cancer. Lifestyle and preventable health conditions can greatly affect risk. Some cancers are not as preventable as others, but there are many habits to adopt to improve our odds.

As we go through the process of determining your level of risk for cancer, it might be clear that your risk is already higher than you want because of factors you cannot change. However, knowledge is power, and you can use that knowledge to be healthy in every other category, to be on heightened alert for any signs of trouble, to stay on schedule for tests and check-ups, and perhaps have advanced screening or genetic testing. There are always steps to take to reduce your risk of cancer and feel your best.

If your history already includes a cancer or high risk for cancer, this way of thinking could lower your risk of it occurring or reoccurring, and your choices could lower the risk of other cancers.

Which category (3, 2 or 1) best represents your goal?

## Cancer POS

| Types/Cancer | Lung | Colorectal | Breast |
|---|---|---|---|
| 3 - <u>Optimal</u> Lowest cancer risk | No smoking ever<br><br>Former smoker, quit ≥20 years ago | ≥50 years with normal colonoscopy<br><br>≤3 servings of red meat per week<br><br>≤1 alcohol servings per day<br><br>Vitamin D & Calcium daily<br><br>Hormone Replacement Therapy<br><br>≥30 minutes of exercise most days | No family history of first-degree relative premenopause breast cancer<br><br>No prior biopsies<br><br>≥30 minutes of exercise per day<br><br>≤1 alcohol servings day<br><br>BMI ≤30<br><br>Screening on schedule<br><br>Mediterranean diet<br><br>*Gail <12.5 and Tyrer-Cuzick <12.5 |
| 2 - <u>Moderate</u> Moderate cancer risk | Quit smoking ≤20 years<br><br>Lived in large city 10+ years<br><br>>50 years old<br><br>Long term secondhand smoke exposure<br>Factory work ≥10 years | History of colon polyps<br><br>Family history of large polyps<br><br>IBS ≥10 years<br><br>≥2 servings of red meat per week | Family history of first-degree menopause breast cancer<br><br>≤30 minutes of exercise per day<br><br>1-2 alcohol servings per day<br><br>BMI ≥30 |

| | | | |
|---|---|---|---|
| | Radiation exposure, COPD, radon exposure | ≥1 alcohol servings per day<br><br>No screening colon-oscopy | *Gail 12-20, Tyrer-Cuzick 12.5-20 |
| 1 - <u>Highest</u><br>Highest cancer risk | Current smoker<br><br>Prior lung cancer<br><br>>30 year pack history<br><br>High risk symptoms: changing cough, short-ness of breath, chest pain, coughing up blood | Personal history co-lon cancer<br><br>First degree relative had colon cancer<br><br>Family cancer syndromes<br><br>Symptoms: blood in stool, change in BM, chronic abdominal pain | Family history of first-degree relative premenopause breast cancer<br><br>Family history male breast cancer<br><br>BRCA 1 or 2+<br><br>Prior breast cancer<br><br>Past high dose radiation<br><br>*Gail ≥20 or Tyrer-Cuzick >20 |

*To find your Gail Model score and Tyrer-Cuzick score, see page 39.

My POS for Cancer risk is _____ (3, 2 or 1)

Why?_____

_____

_____

_____

## D. Diabetes

Pre-diabetes and Type 2 diabetes are preventable. If you already have diabetes, keep-ing your A1C levels low is key to reducing risk for other events such as a heart attack or stroke. Typically, obesity occurs before diabetes begins. Diabetes is a difficult disease on its own, but it also can lead to preventable illness such as central obesity, kidney failure, blindness, nerve damage, sexual problems, foot problems, and many others. Diabetes can be especially hard on women because women with diabetes are more likely to have a heart attack that may be silent at a younger age.

Which category (3, 2 or 1) best represents your goal?

**Diabetes POS**

| 3 - Low risk | • No family history of Type 2 diabetes<br>• Normal fasting blood sugar and glucose tolerance<br>• Waist circumference <35 inches |
|---|---|
| 2 - Moderate risk | • Impaired fasting blood sugar<br>• History of PCOS (Polycystic Ovarian Syndrome)<br>• History of metabolic syndrome<br>• History of gestational diabetes<br>• Family history of Type 2 diabetes<br>• Waist circumference >35 inches<br>• Symptoms of sugar craving and easy weight gain |
| 1 - High risk | • History of Type 2 diabetes<br>• Fasting blood sugar >125 mg/dl<br>• HgA1C >6.5%<br>• Random blood sugar >200 mg/dl |

My POS for Diabetes is _____ (3, 2 or 1)

Why?_____

_____

_____

_____

## E. Ease of Coping: Resilience

There are always issues that need to be dealt with in life. We get in situations where it is not business as usual, and life inevitably has its ups and downs. In the face of trouble with mental or physical health-related issues, relationships, finances, work, children's choices and behavior, how we come out on the other side depends upon our ability to cope, especially for situations in which we have little or no control.

Coping is a combination of inborn skills, learned behavior, and mental health status. We know that people who cope best are able to keep a positive outlook, believe they deserve a good life, and are able to problem solve when times are tough, not only in terms of the problem at hand, but also in terms of how well they are coping. Depression and anxiety, whether more caused by brain neurochemical imbalance or related to difficult situations, can make coping more difficult. People who cope well are willing to ask others for help, believe they deserve to be happy, and maintain a support network of family and friends.

By making the choice of how you want to be able to cope, you are creating intention. Coping, like most skills, can be learned and improved.

Which category (3, 2 or 1) best represents your goal?

### Ease of Coping: Resilience POS

| 3 - Excellent | <ul><li>*PHQ-9 0-4</li><li>Habit of maintaining a positive outlook</li><li>Honest with self and others, ask for help when needed</li><li>Established support group</li></ul> |
|---|---|
| 2 - Moderate | <ul><li>*PHQ-9 5-14</li><li>Currently lost positive outlook</li><li>Increased anxiety or depression</li><li>Some dysfunction in relationships or work because of coping methods, rarely asking for help</li><li>Lost contact with support groups, but they exist</li></ul> |

| 1 - Poor | <ul><li>*PHQ-9 15-27</li><li>Not able to keep positive outlook</li><li>Depression or anxiety</li><li>Relationships in personal life or work very dysfunctional, not asking for help</li><li>No support group</li></ul> |
|---|---|

*To find your PHQ-9 score, see page 48.

My POS for Ease of Coping is _____ (3, 2 or 1)

Why?_____

_____

_____

_____

## F. Phase of Ovarian Function

Menopause and hormone changes happen to all women—how well we do during and after these changes is up to each one of us. Eighty percent of women have at least one significant symptom that affects quality of life. The symptoms can be seen as negative with the power to defeat, or as gifts indicating it is time to get your health and habits on track.

How do you plan on getting through the changes of midlife and menopause? Are you prepared? What is your Picture of Self (POS) during the transition and beyond? There are three possible categories (3, 2 or 1) and eight main symptoms to consider (Hot flashes/night sweats, Libido, Weight, Energy, Moods, Vaginal Dryness/Bladder complaints, and Vaginal Bleeding). You actually do have a choice in how you experience the transition—with or without prescription medication. The symptom scale is called the Menopause Transition Scale™ (MTS) and is used to help determine your POS.

Which category (3, 2 or 1) best represents your goal?

## Phase of Ovarian Function POS

| | |
|---|---|
| 3 - Symptoms are minimal and predictable | • Minimal or rare distress: no or rare hormone-related symptoms<br>• *MTS >19<br>• Knowledge of phase and symptoms |
| 2 - Symptoms are moderate and somewhat predictable | • Symptoms are moderate and predictable<br>• *MTS 12-18 |
| 1 - Symptoms are severe and not predictable | • Able to sometimes predict symptoms and severe distress<br>• *MTS <12<br>• Minimal knowledge of symptom triggers, no knowledge of phases |

*To find your MTS score, see page 67.

My POS for Phase of Ovarian Function is _____ (3, 2 or 1)

Why?_____

_____

_____

_____

## G. Good Bones (Osteoporosis)

Osteoporosis—and the related risk of fracture of the hip, spine, femur, and wrist—is mostly within your control. Your risk at age of menopause and beyond is made up of several factors beyond your control, including family history, ethnicity, and taking certain medications like oral steroids at some point in your life. However, many factors, including alcohol consumption, calcium and Vitamin D intake, and activity level, are (and have been) in your control. Wherever you are now in the scale of risk, you have the opportunity to maintain, gain, or lose bone strength. What do you want? Osteoporosis is a silent but preventable disease. Once you decide your POS and make sure your daily schedule includes ways to keep your goal attainable, you shouldn't have to worry.

Which category (3, 2 or 1) best represents your goal?

## Good Bones POS

| 3- Optimal<br>Low risk for fragile bones<br>and fractures | • Activity of 30 minutes per day<br>• Adequate Vitamin D and calcium<br>• Non-smoker<br>• Two or fewer alcohol servings per day<br>• Menopause and FRAX score less than 3%<br>• Premenopause: 0-2 risk factors |
|---|---|
| 2 - Moderate<br>Moderate risk for fragile bones<br>and fractures | • Premenopause: 3-5 risk factors<br>• Inadequate activity<br>• Inconsistent Vitamin D and calcium<br>• Two or more alcohol servings per day |
| 1- Highest<br>High risk for fragile bones and<br>fractures | • Menopause with prior fragility fractures<br>• Hip or vertebral fracture<br>• FRAX hip >3% or total >20%<br>• Premenopause: 5+ risk factors |

My POS for Good Bones is _____ (3, 2 or 1)

Why?_____

_____

_____

_____

## H. Heart Disease

Heart disease can be prevented or at least delayed. If you were to have a heart attack, your survival and recovery would depend on how healthy you are in other areas—risk for diabetes and stroke, existing activity level, and coping skills. Heart disease is the number one killer of women and it is mostly preventable.

It is easy to think, "Tomorrow I will eat better," or "Tomorrow I will exercise more." However, especially when menopause starts, there are no more make-up days. In other words, every day counts. Here we start at the beginning of how to think about reducing your risk with planning for your desired future. The Reynolds Score will be described more in detail in future chapters; for now go to reynoldsriskscore.org to determine your current score. Many women think, "I will never have a heart attack," or "I am too young for a heart attack," but as heart disease is the leading cause of death in women, prevention requires more than wishful thinking.

Even once a woman has heart disease, she can lower her chance of heart attack or heart failure by changing simple daily habits of exercise, eating healthy, being happy, and getting adequate sleep.

Which category (3, 2 or 1) best represents your goal?

### Heart Disease POS

| 3 - Low risk for heart attack or stroke | <ul><li>Reynolds score <5%</li><li>Heart healthy lifestyle</li><li>No smoking</li><li>Healthy diet with ≤2 red meat servings per week</li><li>Physically active</li><li>BMI ≤30 (Body Mass Index)</li><li>≤7 alcohol servings per week</li></ul> |
| --- | --- |

| 2 - Moderate risk for heart attack or stroke | <ul><li>Reynolds score 5-20%</li><li>Inactivity (≤150 minutes per week)</li><li>BMI ≥30 (Body Mass Index)</li><li>Waist circumference ≥35"</li><li>Family history premature CAD (Coronary Artery Disease)</li><li>High blood pressure controlled</li><li>High LDL or low HDL cholesterol or high triglycerides</li><li>Metabolic syndrome</li><li>Poor exercise capacity</li><li>History of pre-eclampsia</li><li>Gestational diabetes</li><li>PCOS (Polycystic Ovarian Syndrome)</li></ul> |
|---|---|
| 1 - High risk for heart attack or stroke | <ul><li>Reynolds score >20%</li><li>Diagnosed coronary heart disease (microvascular or luminal)</li><li>PAD (Peripheral Arterial Disease)</li><li>CVD (Coronary Vascular Disease)</li><li>High blood pressure not controlled</li><li>Undiagnosed chest pain or shortness of breath</li></ul> |

My POS for Heart Disease is _____ (3, 2 or 1)

Why?_____

_____

_____

_____

## I. Income Security

This category is not about how much money you have or what you are able to buy. It is about your relationship with money and coping with what you have in a realistic way so money does not negatively affect your health and relationships, or add to your stress level. If you are living within your means, know what you have (including a safety net), the stage is set for success—whether that means being mentally freed up to earn more, being happy with what you have, or finding joy in giving to others. Surveys about money and happiness always seem to reach the same conclusions: once people have enough to meet basic needs such as food, shelter, transportation, clothing, and basic entertainment, adding more money does not buy true happiness.

At the milestone event of your choosing, which category of income or financial security do you choose?

Which category (3, 2 or 1) best represents your goal?

### Income Security POS

| 3 - Low risk for financial worry | • Future secured<br>• Savings plan in place<br>• Safety net of at least three months' expenses<br>• Budget in place and followed |
|---|---|
| 2 - Moderate risk for financial worry | • No future plan in place or no professional review<br>• Safety net of three or less months' worth of expenses<br>• Bills paid with budget in place<br>• Low or no credit card balances |
| 1 - High risk for financial worry | • No future plans or savings<br>• No security net<br>• Budget not in place<br>• Some bills go unpaid<br>• High credit card balances and usage |

My POS for Income Security is _____ (3, 2 or 1)

Why?_____

_____

_____

_____

Now that you have broken down your goals by objective measures of wellness, it is time to determine where you stand on your path towards aging like "that!"

# Chapter Five

## *Understanding My Place in Process (PIP)*

Place in Process (PIP) is a way to define where you are, at this moment on your health journey, as you make your way to your milestone event. You might be at your goal now in certain categories of wellness, and way off on others. The only way to get better is to know how far off you are. You can then decide whether you want to adjust your POS or if you want to work to meet your goal in time for the milestone event. This chapter will guide you to understand your current standing in each of the nine categories of wellness.

We will use publicly-available, evidence-based scales to determine your PIP in each category. If you are already at your POS, it makes sense that you would want to continue to maintain and not fall behind. If there is a gap between PIP and POS, the process of W*A*I*Pointes® will help you develop a plan to reach your goals. The LifeMap (Chapter Nine) is a tool to chart your POS and PIP and follow your health journey over time. During the 2009 pilot study of W*A*I*Pointes®, the participants recalculated their PIP every month to check progress and found the process to be very motivating and rewarding.

Let's begin!

### A. Ability to be Active

What is your current activity level and how capable are you of doing the activities you want to do? We use established criteria to determine your PIP in the Ability to be Active category, based on the following factors: the Presidential Fitness Score, your activity across an average week, and by considering the number and type of barriers which make it difficult to reach your goals. Our source for this information is ODPHPH (www.health.gov/).

To complete and calculate your Presidential Fitness Score:

| Presidential Fitness Test | | | | 3, 2, 1 |
|---|---|---|---|---|
| **Aerobic test (do one or the other)** | 1.5 mile run | Time: ____ minutes ____ seconds | Heart rate 60 seconds after stopping: ____ | |
| | 3 mile walk | Time: ____ minutes ____ seconds | Heart rate 60 seconds after stopping: ____ | |
| **Muscular strength: Half sit-ups from flat back, move fingertips 3.5" along ground** | Half-sit ups | ____ in 1 minute | | |
| **Push-up: Flat back, standard on toes, modified on knees** | Push-ups | ____ in 1 minute | | |
| **Flexibility: Use measuring tape from crotch to mark 15" with piece of tape, heels at 14" mark, and note where fingertips end; take best of 3** | Sit and Reach | ____ inches | | |
| **Body composition** | Height: ____ feet ____ inches | Weight: ____ pounds | Waist measurement: ____ inches | |

| Presidential Fitness Score | Age Top Third | Age Middle Third | Age Lower Third |
|---|---|---|---|
| **1.5 mile run (Cooper Institute Norms)** | 40-49: <15:03<br>50-59: <16:46 | 40-49: 15:03-7:38<br>50-59: 16:46-9:43 | 40-49: >17:39<br>50-59: >19:43 |
| **3 mile walk (Cooper Institute Norms)** | 40-49: <39:00<br>50-59: <42:00 | 40-49: 39:00-49:00<br>50-59: 42:00-52:00 | 40-49: >49:00<br>50-59: >52:00 |
| **Muscular strength: half sit-up (Cooper Institute Norms)** | 40-49: >25<br>50-59: >21 | 40-49: 24-19<br>50-59: 20-12 | 40-49: <19<br>50-59: <12 |
| **Muscular strength: Push-up (Cooper Institute Norms)** | 40-49: >13<br>50-59: ND | 40-49: 8-12<br>50-59: ND | 40-49: <8<br>50-59: ND |
| **Flexibility (Cooper Institute Norms)** | 40-49: >19.1 in.<br>50-59: >19.0 in. | 40-49: 19.0-17.0 in.<br>50-59: 18.9-16.0 in. | 40-49: <17.0 in.<br>50-59: <16.0 in. |

PIP Calculation:

Activities of Choice:

_____

_____

_____

Exercise Partners:

_____

_____

_____

Presidential Fitness: _____ (3, 2 or 1)

Activity Level: _____ steps per day

_____ aerobic sessions per week

_____ strength training sessions per week

_____ stretching sessions per week

Barriers to exercise could include schedule constraints, financial constraints for gym or classes, and unsafe neighborhood. Physical constraints could include pain when exercising, being overweight, or illness.

How many barriers do you have? _____

What are your barriers? _____

_____

_____

_____

Which category (3, 2 or 1) best represents your PIP?

## Ability to be Active PIP

| 3 - Very active<br>Presidential Fitness Score<br>>66 percentile (66%) | • More fit than 66% of women your age<br>• Doing more than 10,000 steps per day or more than 110 minutes of aerobic activity per week<br>• Strength training more than 3 times per week<br>• Only the rare barrier keeps you from your plan |
|---|---|

| 2 - Moderately active<br>Presidential Fitness Score<br>>33 percentile (33%) | • More fit than 33% of women your age<br>• Moving between 5,000 and 10,000 steps per day<br>• Strength training 0-2 times per week<br>• 1-3 barriers that could derail you from your plan any day |
|---|---|
| 1 - Barely active<br>Presidential Fitness Score<br><33 percentile (33%) | • Less fit than 33% of women your age<br>• Moving less than 5,000 steps per day<br>• No strength training event per week<br>• 3 or more barriers to activity exist which daily disrupt your chances of activity |

My PIP Ability to be Active is _____ (3, 2 or 1)

## B. Obesity

To determine your PIP, you must first have some base measurements: body fat percentage, BMI, and waist circumference. The first measurement—body fat percentage—can be difficult to get. Your body fat percentage can be measured by a special scale using a VERY low voltage of electrical current to measure your lean mass versus fat mass. This can also be done by doing a skin fold measurement. Many local YMCAs and health clubs offer this as a service, and some doctor's offices, public health offices, and Weight Watcher's offices have the proper equipment. I recommend you call around and find a service—hopefully free or within your budget.

The other measurements are easier to determine. To calculate, you need to weigh yourself and measure your height. To determine your Body Mass Index (BMI), go online at www.calculator.net/body-fat-calculator or call your doctor's office or Public Health Department for assistance.

You will also need to measure your waist circumference. Take a tape measure and measure your waist by first feeling your hip bones and placing the tape just above them and just below your belly button. You can suck it in to make the measurement—we are looking to measure the belly fat you *cannot* suck in!

Diana L. Bitner, MD, NCMP

## Body Fat Percentage Graph

| Age | Low body fat | Healthy Range | Overweight | Obese |
|---|---|---|---|---|
| 20-40 yrs | Under 21% | 21-33% | 33-39% | Over 39% |
| 41-60 yrs | Under 23% | 23-35% | 35-40% | Over 40% |
| 61-79 yrs | Under 24% | 24-36% | 36-42% | Over 42% |

Source: Gallagher et al. Am J Clin Nut 2000; 72:694-701

Body fat percentage: _____% (from chart above)

BMI: _____ www.calculator.net/body-fat-calculator (This is an estimate, more accurate in the clinic with the impedance scale.)

Waist circumference: _____ inches

These are the three categories; use your measurements to determine your PIP.

Which category (3, 2 or 1) best represents your PIP?

### Obesity PIP

| 3 - Healthy | • Waist circumference <35 inches<br>• BMI <25.0<br>• Body fat percentage in healthy range for your age (20-40: 21-33%, 41-60: 23-35%, and 61-79: 24-36%) |
|---|---|
| 2 - Overweight | • Waist circumference between 35-39 inches<br>• BMI between 25-29.9<br>• Body fat percentage in overweight range (20-40: 33-39%, 41-60: 35-40%, 61-79: 36-42%) |

| 1 - Obese | • Waist circumference 40 inches<br>• BMI >30<br>• Body fat percentage obese (20-40: >39%, 41-60: >40%, 61-79: >42%) |
|---|---|

My Obesity PIP is _____ (3, 2 or 1)

## C. Cancer

This is a complicated category! As described in the *I Want To Age Like That!* book, cancer risk scales can be controversial and not totally accurate, and some factors matter more than others. Risk scales should be used carefully. These scales should be used as a call to action, an approximate risk assessor to then use with your doctor to make any formal action plans with referrals to specialists or genetic testing. It is a guide to help you think about your choices and be informed to make the best lifestyle choices and get cancer or genetic screening tests. So many people make uninformed choices all day long that could unknowingly increase cancer risk.

The most common cancers affecting women are cancer of the lung, colon and rectum, and breast. Knowledge is power and prevention is possible!

Complete this PIP worksheet by filling in the blanks and circling the correct answers.

### Lung cancer risk

Your age:                _____

Present height:          _____

Present weight:          _____

BMI:                     _____

Smoking history:

    Do you smoke?                                      Y   N

      No—Did you ever smoke?                        Y   N

      Yes—How long have you smoked?          _____

How much do you smoke now? _____

How long ago did you quit? _____

Personal history of lung cancer?　　　　　Y　N

    No—Go to next question.

    Yes—When? _____

    What treatment did you have? _____

_____

_____

Do you have COPD or Pulmonary Fibrosis?　　　Y　N

Family history of lung cancer?　　　　　Y　N

    No—Go to next question.

    Yes—Who and at what age? _____

_____

_____

_____

_____

Have you lived with a smoker most of your life?　　Y　N

Have you lived in/near a large city for at least ten years of your life?　Y　N

Have you ever had any <u>unprotected</u> exposure to any of the following?

    Asbestos?　　　　　Y　N

    Radiation?　　　　　Y　N

    Radon?　　　　　Y　N

      Have you had your home tested for radon?　Y　N

Have you ever worked in a factory or foundry?                           Y     N

If you answered yes to any of the above, explain:

_____

_____

_____

_____

Do you eat five or more servings of fruits and vegetables per day?      Y     N

Do you currently have any of these symptoms?

    Changing cough?                                  Y     N

    Coughing up blood?                               Y     N

    Chest pain?                                      Y     N

    Shortness of breath?                             Y     N

    Unexplained weight loss?                         Y     N

    Unexplained back pain?                           Y     N

**Colorectal cancer risk**

Personal history of colon cancer?                                       Y     N

    No—Go to next question.

    Yes—When? _____

First-degree family history of colorectal cancer?                       Y     N

    No—Go to next question.

    Yes—Who and at what age? _____

Amount of time taking birth control pills or hormone therapy? _____

_____

Daily aspirin use of 15 or more years?                                    Y   N

Personal history of Inflammatory Bowel Disease such as
Crohn's Disease?                                                          Y   N

      No—Go to next question.

      Yes—For how long? _____

Three or more servings of red meat per week? (4 ounce serving)            Y   N

Alcohol quantity and frequency: How many 4 ounce servings of alcohol or wine, or 8 ounce servings of beer do you consume per week? _____

Do you take a daily multivitamin?                                         Y   N

      With folate?                                          Y   N

Do you take a daily calcium supplement?                                   Y   N

      How many servings of dairy on a typical day?    _____

Do you exercise three or more hours per week?                             Y   N

Do you currently have any of these symptoms?

      Unexplained rectal bleeding?                          Y   N

      New onset diarrhea/constipation?                      Y   N

      Change in stool appearance?                           Y   N

      Abdominal pain for more than two weeks without
      explanation?                                          Y   N

Do you have a family history of polyps?                                   Y   N

Do you have a personal history of colon polyps?                           Y   N

## Breast Cancer Risk

Breast cancer risk assessment: Validated risk evaluation tools exist to help guide your next steps. These tools are helpful to assess whether additional screening would be worthwhile, whether genetic testing is indicated, or whether medication to reduce risk would be indicated. The Tyrer-Cuzick Model (ems-trials.org/riskevaluator) is valuable because it considers details of family history and breast density. When you visit this website, click on Software Downloads and then click on Current Version to download the most updated version on your computer. Answer the questions to determine your risk. If you have further questions, print out the evaluation and take it to your physician to discuss in more detail.

Another valuable tool, the Gail Model (cancer.gov/bcrisktool/) is used to consider risk-reducing medications.

Genetics/History:

What is your race/ethnicity? _____

    Does your ancestry include Jewish heritage?           Y   N

Do you have a personal history of breast or ovarian cancer?      Y   N

    No—Go to next question.

    Yes—Explain with regard to what type, when you had it, how it was detected, treatment you received, etc.

_____

_____

_____

_____

Family history of breast, ovarian, or prostate cancer?      Y   N

    No—Go to next question.

    Yes—Explain with regard to what type, who had it, how it was detected, treatment received, etc.

_____

_____

_____

Age of first menstrual period? _____

Number of term pregnancies? _____

Your age(s) when you gave birth to each child.

_____

_____

_____

_____

Did you breastfeed?                                        Y    N

    No—Go to next question.

    Yes—For how long for each child? _____

    _____

    _____

    _____

    _____

Have you ever had breast biopsies?                         Y    N

    No—Go to next question.

    Yes—Normal or abnormal? _____

BRCA (1, 2) gene mutation? (high risk for breast cancer)   Y    N

    Have you been tested?                                  Y    N

Your weight at age 18? _____

Are you currently using hormone therapy?                   Y    N

    No—Go to next question.

    Yes—For how long? _____

Have you used hormone therapy for menopause?                          Y    N

    No—Go to next question.

    Yes—For how long? _____

What is your current Phase of Ovarian Function:
regular periods, perimenopause, or menopause? _____

Did you use Tamoxifen(R) or Raloxifen for five or more years?         Y    N

Do you have a history of benign/fibrocystic breast disease?          Y    N

Was your birth weight greater than 8.5 pounds?                       Y    N

Do you have regular mammograms?                                      Y    N

BI-RADS score (from your most recent mammogram report); density
classification = BIRADS 1-5? _____

Do you have dense breasts?                                           Y    N

What is your Gail Model Risk score? _____

What is your Tyrer-Cuzick score? _____

Fill in scores below:

Your five-year risk:              Gail: _____    Tyrer-Cuzick: _____

The average five-year risk:       Gail: _____    Tyrer-Cuzick: _____

Your lifetime risk:               Gail: _____    Tyrer-Cuzick: _____

The average lifetime risk:        Gail: _____    Tyrer-Cuzick: _____

Which category (3, 2 or 1) best represents your PIP?

## Cancer PIP

| Types/Cancer | Lung | Colorectal | Breast |
|---|---|---|---|
| 3 - Optimal risk for cancer of lung, colorectal and breast | No smoking ever<br><br>Former smoker, quit ≥20 years ago | Normal colonoscopy ≥50 years<br><br>≤3 servings red meat per week<br><br>≤1 alcohol servings per day<br><br>Vitamin D & calcium daily<br><br>≥30 minutes of exercise most days | No family history of first-degree relative premenopause breast cancer<br><br>No prior biopsies<br><br>≥30 minutes exercise per day<br><br>≤1 alcohol servings per day<br><br>BMI ≤30<br><br>Screening up to date<br><br>Mediterranean Diet<br><br>Gail <12.5, Tyrer-Cuzick <12.5 |
| 2 - Moderate risk for cancer of lung, colorectal, or breast | Quit smoking ≤20 years<br><br>Lived in large city 10+ years<br><br>Long term second-hand smoke exposure<br><br>Factory work ≥10 years<br><br>Radiation exposure | History of colon polyps<br><br>Family history of large polyps<br><br>IBS ≥10 years<br><br>≥2 servings of red meat per week<br><br>≥1 alcohol servings per day | Family history of first- degree relative premenopause breast cancer<br><br>≤30 minutes exercise per day<br><br>1-2 alcohol servings per day<br><br>BMI ≥30 |

| | | No screening for colonoscopy | Gail 12-20, Tyrer-Cuzick 12.5-20 |
|---|---|---|---|
| 1 - High risk for cancer of lung, colorectal, or breast | Current smoker<br><br>Prior lung cancer<br><br>High risk symptoms: changing cough, shortness of breath, chest pain, coughing up blood | Personal history of colon cancer<br><br>First-degree relative had colon cancer<br><br>Family cancer syndromes<br><br>Symptoms: blood in stool, change in BM, chronic abdominal pain | Family history of first-degree relative pre-menopause breast cancer<br><br>Family history male breast cancer<br><br>BRCA 1 or 2+<br><br>Prior breast cancer<br><br>Past chest high dose radiation<br><br>Gail ≥20, Tyrer-Cuzick >20 |

My Lung Cancer PIP is _____ (3, 2 or 1)

My Colorectal Cancer PIP is _____ (3, 2 or 1)

My Breast Cancer PIP is _____ (3, 2 or 1)

My overall PIP for Cancer is _____ (use lowest of 3 scores)

## D. Diabetes

Diabetes is difficult to deal with on its own, and is a major risk factor for early death, heart disease, stroke, obesity, and uterine cancer. In addition, associated belly fat can cause facial hair and male-pattern baldness. Here we determine your level of risk for diabetes. Complete this PIP worksheet by circling the correct answer and filling in the blanks.

Do you currently have any of these symptoms?

Overwhelming sugar/carb craving?                                     Y     N

Confusing weight gain?                                           Y   N

Do you have a history of gestational diabetes mellitus
(pregnancy-induced)?                                             Y   N

Do you have a family history of Type 2 diabetes?                Y   N

What is your waist circumference? _____

What is your waist-hip ratio? _____

Have you had lab work done in the last six months?              Y   N

No—it's time to get tested.

Yes—answer the following:

What was your fasting blood sugar? _____

What was your HgA1C? _____

Which category (3, 2 or 1) best represents your PIP?

**Diabetes PIP**

| 3 - Low risk | • No family history of Type 2 diabetes<br>• Normal fasting blood sugar and glucose tolerance<br>• Waist circumference <35 inches |
|---|---|
| 2 - Moderate risk | • Impaired fasting blood sugar<br>• History of PCOS (Polycystic Ovarian Syndrome)<br>• History of *metabolic syndrome<br>• History of gestational diabetes<br>• Family history of Type 2 diabetes<br>• Waist circumference >35 inches<br>• Symptoms of sugar craving and easy weight gain |
| 1 - High risk | • History of Type 2 diabetes<br>• Fasting blood sugar >125 mg/dl<br>• HgA1C >6.5%<br>• Random blood sugar >200 mg/dl |

*Metabolic syndrome - obesity, high blood pressure, high cholesterol and high blood sugar

My Diabetes PIP is _____ (3, 2 or 1)

## E. Ease of Coping

Everyone has issues, difficulties, and challenges, and some women cope better than others. Coping skills can help us weather the storms of illness; separation; empty nest; and changes in jobs, living arrangements, financials, or relationships. Have you ever considered the quality of your coping skills? Now is the time to make sure you are ready for the next challenge.

Coping is a combination of inborn skills, learned behavior, and mental health. Research shows that people who cope successfully tend to believe they deserve to be happy, are good at asking for help, and stay connected with a network of supportive friends and family. Unfortunately, coping can be thrown off by symptoms of depression or anxiety, abuse of alcohol or drugs, or medical problems. And, coping skills can be challenged by illness; being emotionally, sexually, or physically abused; or financial need.

To assess your ability to cope, the first step is to think about your perception of your coping skills.

Do you cope well in tough situations?                                          Y    N

Who are your coping mentors (mom, grandmother, teacher, friend, great aunt, etc.)?_____

_____

Do you want to learn to cope better?                                          Y    N

Here in this workbook, I want you to consider your coping skills as you complete several tasks. These include:

• Taking the Brief COPE Questionnaire.

• Taking the CAGE Alcohol Questionnaire and marking your score below.

- Taking the Patient Health Questionnaire-9 (PHQ-9) to screen for depression/anxiety.

- Taking the online Health-Related Quality of Life Quiz (HRQOL-14) at https://www.cdc.gov/hrqol/hrqol14_measure.htm.

## Brief COPE Questionnaire

Here in this workbook, I want you to consider your coping skills by completing several tasks. These will assess your type of coping skills, your level of mood disturbance and risk for depression, and risk of having a problem with abuse of alcohol. The good news is that by identifying and acknowledging your skills at dealing with difficult situations, it might be an awakening to why you are not able to live the life you would want. This is an opportunity to seek out skills which could get you closer to aging like you want!

Start with a modified Brief COPE Quiz. It is used by psychologists and was developed by Dr. Carver of the University of Miami to assess people's methods of coping with hardship and to use the answers to discuss what works and what does not work. There are no right or wrong answers. The information is meant to be used in self-discovery and analysis.

In answering the questionnaire below, think about a recent event in your life when you needed to use coping skills.

Mark your answers with as much truth as possible and use 1: not at all, 2: a little bit, 3: medium amount, 4: mostly.

X ____ 1. Turned to work or other activities to take my mind off things.

O ____ 2. Concentrated my efforts on doing something about the situation I'm in.

X ____ 3. Said to myself, "This isn't real."

X ____ 4. Used alcohol or other drugs to make myself feel better.

O ____ 5. Got emotional support from others.

X ____ 6. Gave up trying to deal with it.

O ____ 7. Took action to try to make the situation better.

X ____ 8. Refused to believe it had happened.

X ____ 9. Used alcohol or other drugs to help me get through it.

X ____ 10. Criticized myself.

O ____ 11. Realized that my feelings are valid and important.

O ____12. Got comfort and understanding from someone.

X ____13. Gave up the attempt to cope.

O ____14. Looked for something good in what was happening.

X ____15. Made jokes about it.

X ____16. Did something to think about it less, such as going to the movies, watching tv, reading, day dreaming, sleeping, or shopping.

O ____ 17. Allowed myself to express my emotions.

O ____ 18. Tried to get advice or help from other people about what to do.

X ____ 19. Learned to live with it.

X ____ 20. Blamed myself for things that happened.

O ____ 21. Prayed or meditated.

Add the total X and O answers.

**X = Total: _____      O = Total: _____**


## CAGE Questionnaire for Detecting Alcoholism:

| Question | Yes | No |
|---|---|---|
| Have you ever felt you should **C**ut down on your drinking? | 1 | 0 |
| Have people **A**nnoyed you by criticizing your drinking? | 1 | 0 |
| Have you felt **G**uilty about your drinking? | 1 | 0 |

| Have you ever had a drink first thing in the morning (**E**ye opener)? | **1** | **0** |
|---|---|---|

Total score _____

   0 or 1 Low risk of problem drinking
   2 or 3 High suspicion for alcoholism
   4       Likely diagnostic of alcoholism

*Reference: Ewing JA, Detecting Alcoholism: The CAGE Questionnaire JAMA 1984 252(14) 1905-7*

## Patient Health Questionnaire-9 (PHQ-9)

Over the last two weeks, have you been bothered by any of the following problems?

0 = Not at all, 1 = Several days, 2 = More than half the days, 3 = Most days

____1. Little interest or pleasure in doing things.

____2. Feeling down, depressed, or hopeless.

____3. Trouble falling or staying asleep, or sleeping too much.

____4. Feeling tired or having little energy.

____5. Poor appetite or overeating.

____6. Feeling bad about yourself—or that you are a failure or have let yourself or your family down.

____7. Trouble concentrating on things, such as reading the newspaper or watching television

____8. Moving or speaking so slowly that other people could have noticed; or the opposite—being so fidgety or restless that you have been moving around a lot more than usual.

____9. Thoughts that you would be better off dead or of hurting yourself in some way.

PHQ-9 Score _____

    0-4 Minimal depression

    5-9 Mild depression

    10-14 Moderate depression

    15+ Warrants treatment

*Developed by Drs. Robert L. Spitzer, Janet B.W. Williams, Kurt Kroenke and colleagues, with an educational grant from Pfizer Inc. No permission required to reproduce, translate, display or distribute.*

Which category (3, 2 or 1) best represents your PIP?

**Ease of Coping PIP**

| 3 - Healthy | <ul><li>Cope: O>X score</li><li>PHQ-9 0-4</li><li>Habit of maintaining a positive outlook</li><li>Honest, able to ask for help</li><li>Have established support group, maintain contact</li></ul> |
|---|---|
| 2 - Moderate | <ul><li>Cope: O=X</li><li>PHQ-9 5-14</li><li>Currently lost positive outlook</li><li>Increased anxiety</li><li>Some dysfunction in relationships or work because of coping methods</li><li>Lost contact with support group, but they exist</li></ul> |
| 1 - Poor | <ul><li>Cope: O<X</li><li>PHQ-9 15-27</li><li>Not able to keep positive outlook</li><li>Depression or anxiety crippling relationships or work</li><li>No support group</li></ul> |

My Ease of Coping PIP is _____ (3, 2 or 1)

Diana L. Bitner, MD, NCMP

## F. Phase of Ovarian Function

Your midlife and menopause symptoms can be used as a vital sign to determine how healthy you are, almost like your blood pressure or heart rate. Symptoms are also associated with hormone levels and reflect daily habits and lifestyle. Frequent and severe symptoms can make it more difficult to do healthy habits; a bad night's sleep caused by three bad sweats will make it very difficult to get up and exercise in the morning. Perimenopause and menopause can be vicious, confusing periods of time of unnecessary suffering. If this describes your life, rest assured you are not alone and this information will help! This will clear up the confusion and help you feel better.

At this point, go to page 67 and get your Menopause Transition Scale™ score.

Total possible MTS: _____/21

Which category (3, 2 or 1) best represents your PIP?

### Phase of Ovarian Function PIP

| 3 - Symptoms are minimal and predictable | • Minimal or rare distress: no or mild hormone-related symptoms<br>• MTS >19<br>• Knowledge of phase and symptoms |
|---|---|
| 2 - Symptoms are moderate and somewhat predictable | • Symptoms mild and predictable<br>• MTS 12-18 |
| 1 - Symptoms are severe, not predictable | • Sometimes able to predict symptoms and severe distress<br>• MTS <12<br>• Minimal knowledge of symptom triggers, no knowledge of phases |

My Phase of Ovarian Function PIP is _____ (3, 2 or 1)

## G. Good Bones—Osteoporosis and risk of fracture

Low bone density and fragility fractures—or fractures with minimal trauma—are often preventable, and even if you have low bone density, you can lower your chances of a

50

broken bone by maintaining your fitness and balance with exercise, yoga, Tai Chi, etc. If you are not in menopause, your Good Bones category PIP is determined by adding up risk factors (see page 52), and if you are in menopause, your Good Bones PIP is determined by the FRAX score which is available online. To determine your score, collect the information below and then go online to www.sheffield.ac.uk/FRAX. At the top of the page is the Calculation Tool tab. Click on your location, answer the questions and click on Calculate. Based on the calculations, fill in the information below.

Age: _____

Height: _____

Weight: _____

BMI: _____

DEXA (bone density test to be ordered by your health care provider) score of _____

Please answer the following risk factor questions about yourself:

| | | |
|---|---|---|
| Fragility fractures since 50? | Y | N |
| Rheumatoid arthritis? | Y | N |
| Currently smoking? | Y | N |
| Two or more alcoholic drinks per day? | Y | N |
| Cortisone use of 5mg or more for three or more months? | Y | N |
| Physically active for 30 minutes three or more times per week? | Y | N |
| Parental history of hip fractures? | Y | N |

Do you have any of these Secondary Risk Factors for Osteoporosis?

| | | |
|---|---|---|
| Type 1 diabetes. | Y | N |
| Hyperthyroidism or over-use of thyroid medication. | Y | N |
| Premature menopause (<40 without hormone replacement therapy). | Y | N |

Premenopausal: # risk factors: _____ (Add the number of Y answers)

In menopause: Using your score from the FRAX website, the ten year probability of:

    A.  Risk of major osteoporotic fracture: _____

    B.  Risk of hip fracture: _____

Use the information collected above and correspond with the information in the graph below.

Which category (3, 2, or 1) best represents your PIP?

**Good Bones PIP**

| 3 - Low risk for fragile bones and fracture | <ul><li>Activity of 30 minutes per day</li><li>Adequate Vitamin D and calcium</li><li>Non-smoker</li><li>Two or fewer alcohol servings per day</li><li>FRAX hip <3% or total <20%</li><li>Premenopause 0-2 risk factors</li></ul> |
|---|---|
| 2 - Moderate risk for fragile bones and fracture | <ul><li>Premenopause 3-5 risk factors</li><li>Activity <30 minutes per day</li><li>Inconsistent Vitamin D and calcium</li><li>FRAX hip <3% or total <20%</li></ul> |
| 1 - High risk for fragile bones and fracture | <ul><li>Menopause with prior fragility fracture</li><li>Prior hip or vertebral fracture</li><li>FRAX hip >3% or total >20%</li><li>Premenopause 5+ risk factors</li><li>Fear of falling which limits activity</li></ul> |

My Good Bones PIP is _____ (3, 2 or 1)

**H. Heart Disease**

Heart Disease (also known as Cardiovascular Disease or CVD) is the number one killer of women—one in three women will die of heart disease, either by heart attack, heart failure, or stroke. The good news is that CVD is preventable for most women, and if already present, the risk for a bad event can be minimized with both a healthy lifestyle and medications that can lower cholesterol, treat high blood sugar and drop high blood pressure. By determining your PIP, you will have the knowledge to improve your quality of life and affect how long you live.

Please answer the following questions about yourself based on your history or most recent health care report.

Currently a cigarette smoker?          Y   N

Systolic blood pressure (top number)    _____ mm/Hg

HDL level    _____ mg/DL

Total cholesterol    _____ mg/DL

High Sensitivity C-reactive Protein    _____ mg/L

Family history of mother or father with
heart attack after the age of 60?    Y   N

      Reynolds score (reynoldsriskscore.org)  _____

Are you currently diabetic?    Y   N

    No—Go to next question.

    If Yes:

        Is it controlled?    Y   N

Hemoglobin AIC (measure of blood sugar level over three months)?  _____

Persistent high LDL while taking statin?    Y   N

High blood pressure poorly controlled?    Y   N

Unexplained chest pain or shortness of breath with exertion?    Y   N

Do you have metabolic syndrome (obesity, high blood pressure,
high cholesterol and high blood sugar)?    Y   N

Waist circumference 35" or more?                                     Y   N

BP 130/85 or higher? (or being treated for hypertension?)           Y   N

Triglycerides 150 or higher?                                         Y   N

HDL below 50?                                                        Y   N

Fasting blood sugar 100 or higher?                                   Y   N

Which category (3, 2 or 1) best represents your PIP?

**Heart Disease PIP**

| 3 - Low risk for heart attack or stroke | • Reynolds score <5%<br>• No smoking<br>• Healthy diet with ≤2 red meat servings per week<br>• Physically active<br>• BMI ≤30<br>• ≤7 alcohol servings per week |
|---|---|
| 2 - Moderate risk for heart attack or stroke | • Reynolds score 5-20%<br>• Inactivity (≤150 minutes per week)<br>• BMI ≥30<br>• Waist circumference ≥35"<br>• Family history premature CAD (Coronary Artery Disease)<br>• High blood pressure controlled<br>• High LDL or low HDL cholesterol or high triglycerides<br>• Metabolic syndrome<br>• Poor exercise capacity<br>• History of pre-eclampsia<br>• Gestational diabetes<br>• PCOS (Polycystic Ovarian Syndrome) |
| 1- High risk for heart attack or stroke | • Reynolds score >20%<br>• Diagnosed coronary heart disease (microvascular or luminal)<br>• PAD (diagnosed Peripheral Arterial Disease)<br>• CVD (diagnosed Cerebral Vascular Disease) |

| | • High blood pressure not controlled<br>• Undiagnosed chest pain or shortness of breath |
|---|---|

My Heart Disease PIP is _____ (3, 2 or 1)

## I. Income Security

How can you sleep well if you are up all night worrying about how to pay your bills or what you will do in retirement? Your feeling of security about money can affect your health in many ways; therefore, it deserves our attention as a separate category of wellness. This is not about how much you have but what you do with the resources you do have. Being financially secure is possible. Being organized, clear, and knowledgeable about your finances can help you live better.

| | | |
|---|---|---|
| Do you have a job? Or regular income? | Y | N |
| Do you have a budget? | Y | N |
| If you have a budget, do you follow your plan? | Y | N |
| Do you balance your checkbook? | Y | N |
| Do you frequently spend more than you have? | Y | N |
| Do you keep credit card debt more than one month? | Y | N |
| Do you have a retirement plan? And utilize your company's matching benefits? | Y | N |
| Do you have an emergency fund? | Y | N |
| 0-2 months expenses | Y | N |
| 3-6 months expenses | Y | N |
| >6 months expenses | Y | N |
| Are you past due on bills? | Y | N |

Use the information collected above and correspond with the information in the graph on the next page.

Which category (3, 2 or 1) best represents your PIP?

**Income Security PIP**

| 3 - Low risk for financial worry | • Future secured with retirement fund and professional review<br>• Savings plan in place<br>• Safety net of at least three months' worth of expenses<br>• Budget in place and followed |
|---|---|
| 2 - Moderate risk for financial worry | • Retirement plan in place with professional review<br>• Safety net of three or less months' worth of expenses<br>• Bills paid but not following budget<br>• Low or no credit card balances |
| 1 - High risk for financial worry | • No future plans or savings<br>• No security net<br>• Budget not in place<br>• Some bills go unpaid<br>• High credit card balances and usage |

My Income Security PIP is _____ (3, 2 or 1)

Determining your PIP can be surprising, confusing, alarming, scary, or encouraging. Now that you have determined your current state in the nine categories of wellness, it is time to get to work either maintaining your PIP because it matches your POS, getting your PIP to rise to match your POS, or changing your goals. How do you feel right now? Place your PIP scores on the LifeMap chart (next page) and make your plan. Great job so far!

**LifeMap:** Place an X in the corresponding box for your POS at the age you chose for your milestone event, and an O in the corresponding box for your PIP at your current age. You can then decide how to reach your POS by looking at your barriers and making a plan using your LifeMap, or readjust your POS. This is up to you. We will support you reaching your goals.

| PIP/POS | | | | | | | | | | | | | | | | | | |
|---|---|---|---|---|---|---|---|---|---|---|---|---|---|---|---|---|---|
| 27 | | | | | | | | | | | | | | | | | |
| 26 | | | | | | | | | | | | | | | | | |
| 25 | | | | | | | | | | | | | | | | | |
| 24 | | | | | | | | | | | | | | | | | |
| 23 | | | | | | | | | | | | | | | | | |
| 22 | | | | | | | | | | | | | | | | | |
| 21 | | | | | | | | | | | | | | | | | |
| 20 | | | | | | | | | | | | | | | | | |
| 19 | | | | | | | | | | | | | | | | | |
| 18 | | | | | | | | | | | | | | | | | |
| 17 | | | | | | | | | | | | | | | | | |
| 16 | | | | | | | | | | | | | | | | | |
| 15 | | | | | | | | | | | | | | | | | |
| 14 | | | | | | | | | | | | | | | | | |
| 13 | | | | | | | | | | | | | | | | | |
| 12 | | | | | | | | | | | | | | | | | |
| 11 | | | | | | | | | | | | | | | | | |
| 10 | | | | | | | | | | | | | | | | | |
| 9 | | | | | | | | | | | | | | | | | |
| AGE | 18 | 25 | 30 | 35 | 40 | 45 | 50 | 55 | 60 | 65 | 70 | 75 | 80 | 85 | 90 | 95 | 100 |

See example of how to complete your LifeMap on the next page.

Example of the LifeMap for a 50-year-old woman with a PIP of 21 (X) and a POS of 24 (O) at age 65.

| PIP/POS | | | | | | | | | | | | | | | | | |
|---|---|---|---|---|---|---|---|---|---|---|---|---|---|---|---|---|
| 27 | | | | | | | | | | | | | | | | | |
| 26 | | | | | | | | | | | | | | | | | |
| 25 | | | | | | | | | | | | | | | | | |
| 24 | | | | | | | | | O | | | | | | | | |
| 23 | | | | | | | | | | | | | | | | | |
| 22 | | | | | | | | | | | | | | | | | |
| 21 | | | | | | | X | | | | | | | | | | |
| 20 | | | | | | | | | | | | | | | | | |
| 19 | | | | | | | | | | | | | | | | | |
| 18 | | | | | | | | | | | | | | | | | |
| 17 | | | | | | | | | | | | | | | | | |
| 16 | | | | | | | | | | | | | | | | | |
| 15 | | | | | | | | | | | | | | | | | |
| 14 | | | | | | | | | | | | | | | | | |
| 13 | | | | | | | | | | | | | | | | | |
| 12 | | | | | | | | | | | | | | | | | |
| 11 | | | | | | | | | | | | | | | | | |
| 10 | | | | | | | | | | | | | | | | | |
| 9 | | | | | | | | | | | | | | | | | |
| AGE | 18 | 25 | 30 | 35 | 40 | 45 | 50 | 55 | 60 | 65 | 70 | 75 | 80 | 85 | 90 | 95 | 100 |

The next chapter is about understanding, charting, and improving your health habits, also known as the Seven Essential Elements of Daily Success (SEEDS®). The SEEDS® are crucial to helping you feel good and reach your goals. These are the basic habits of deliberate wellbeing. By using practical tips from years of my medical practice and personal experience, you can improve how often you can live your true self.

# Chapter Six
## *Feeling Better Using the SEEDS®*
## *The Seven Essential Elements of Daily Success*

The Seven Essential Elements of Daily Success, or SEEDS®, are the "basics habits" that impact how well women will age and feel. Bottom line: If you get all your SEEDS® accomplished every day, the result will be to feel better and be healthier. The SEEDS® are daily reminders to make sure you are doing what you need to do to live your true life. If you have a hot flash or feel very tired, chances are the symptom can be tracked back to a lack of one or more of the SEEDS®. There is no magic pill for anti-aging and the SEEDS® do work when you follow them.

If you are not meeting your daily SEEDS®, it likely means you have barriers in the way. These barriers are not excuses; instead, they are explanations. If you face your barriers as hurdles to overcome—a busy schedule, lack of money for a gym membership, or insomnia—then you will be more likely to be successful.

Just as if you were sitting in my office, let's talk about each of the SEEDS® categories.

### 1. <u>Water—Eight 10 oz glasses every day</u>

First, we all have slightly different water requirements based on our body size, physical activity, and metabolism. This recommendation is meant as a guide—it may vary slightly for each person. Second, add a serving of water for each serving of caffeine or alcohol taken in that day to finish with a net of eight servings at the end of each day. Many of us have challenges with schedules that can affect when we can drink water and when we can empty our bladders. If you work in a factory, are a teacher, or perform surgery, timing is everything. It simply takes more planning. Perhaps a plan could be as follows:

- Drink two or three glasses of water before leaving the house.

- Drink one more in the car on the way to work or school.

- Drink a glass of water as your day begins and schedule a bathroom break when it works best for you.

- Several hours later, make time for another glass of water and another bathroom break.

- Drink one more glass at lunch and again during your afternoon break.

- Plan on drinking one more in the car on the way home and perhaps one more with dinner or when you exercise.

- Done!

A good rule of thumb is that it takes three days to hydrate and three days to dehydrate. When we are well hydrated, it shows—shiny, strong hair, fewer wrinkles, and good energy. It is best to start a hydration process on the weekend because of more frequent urination at the onset. Also, drinking more water the day before a big workout or a long day can help improve energy and performance. I recommend putting water on your schedule like any other event.

## 2. **Sleep—50 hours every week**

Sleep is everything—this cannot be underestimated! Adequate sleep improves performance, memory, and energy levels; and reduces the risk of illness, disease, dementia, depression, or anxiety. It must be a priority. We all get busy and think that cutting corners on sleep is the best way to catch up on our to-do list. The goal is to get two sleep cycles of 3-4 hours each, or about seven hours of solid sleep every night. If you have serious concerns about your ability to get good sleep, it is best to talk to your doctor or a sleep specialist. Serious conditions such as sleep apnea are treatable and can impact your risk for serious health conditions such as heart attack. For the more routine concerns, there are practical tricks that work when put into practice.

If the issue is falling asleep, the issue is likely poor sleep hygiene. This is the official term for set steps to take before falling asleep. It is important to have a routine, avoid screen time 15 to 30 minutes before wanting to fall asleep, and be consistent. It can also be good practice to have bed be only for sleep or sex—not TV, reading, working, etc. Our bodies are creatures of habit and need to know bed is for sleep. Also, many women say they have difficulty falling asleep due to mind-racing once their head hits the pillow. The answer? Follow a routine.

**Example routine:**

- Finish daily chores (pack lunches, clean kitchen, desk work, etc.).

- Review the weekly to-do list, the daily to-do list, and make the to-do list for the next day.

- Relax (read, watch TV, have sex, etc.).

- Do your bathroom routine (wash face, take a shower, brush your teeth, etc.).

- Go to your Zen spot in the house (where you can be by yourself), and get comfortable. When you are very comfortable, think of three things you are grateful for, and do yoga or "metered breathing." Here's a how-to for metered breathing: As you get settled into your comfortable position, stare at a specific spot (on the wall, the floor, the ceiling, etc.); close your mouth; and breathe through your nose, focusing on the sound of your breath. Then, get in your bed, snuggle up, and go to sleep. If you lay there and start to worry, get back up, return to your Zen spot, think about your gratitudes, and do some more yoga or metered breathing. It works!

If the issue is waking up in the middle of the night (usually three and one-half hours after falling sleep), it generally means you had alcohol before bed (and it wore off), had a hot flash that woke you up, or something disturbed you (partner snoring or a big worry). Hopefully you go right back to sleep. But, if not, the trick is to NOT "catastrophize" or worry about being awake. Instead, think to yourself, "I've got this!" Get up right away, go to the bathroom, drink a glass of water, go out to your Zen spot, and repeat your bedtime ritual of gratitudes and metered breathing. Then go back to bed and go to sleep. If it does not work, get back up and do it again. Even three cycles of this practice is better than two hours awake and the alarm going off 20 minutes after you got to sleep. Good habits are possible—it just takes practice.

### 3. <u>Vitamins—Multivitamin, Vitamin D, Calcium</u>

Vitamin supplements are helpful to ensure you are getting daily basic requirements in the case your diet is not adequate on a daily basis. I am not a dietician and am staying very basic for this discussion. From all my reading and learning at medical meetings, I believe the easiest way to satisfy your body requirements is to take a daily multivitamin—any one that agrees with your stomach and fits your budget. Calcium is the most important building block for bones, and adequate daily calcium is important to avoid osteoporosis and fractures. The best source for calcium is your diet, not a pill. Too much calcium can increase the risk of kidney stones and heart disease by calcifying existing vessel plaque. Approximately 1,200 mg per day from dietary sources is best. Vitamin D is very important for bone health and thought to impact inflammation, cancer risk, and health of blood vessels (studies in progress) and can be difficult to get from food sources; it is best when taken as a soft gel or drops. The average woman (based on weight) requires approximately 2,000 IU per day. Ongoing research will better quantify the dose (vitaltrial.org), but this dose is a good starting point. Your doctor can order a blood test if there are questions about absorption (i.e., if you had bariatric surgery).

### 4. <u>Fiber—35 grams per day</u>

Fiber is classified as either soluble or insoluble, and both are healthy additions to a daily diet. Insoluble fiber, such as the skin of an apple or the husk on wheat or rice, is helpful to keep bowel movements formed. Adequate intake of insoluble fiber is associated with less constipation and less colon cancer. Soluble fiber is the inside of the apple, many fruits, and oatmeal. It helps reduce cholesterol and slow sugar absorption. A healthy diet should be approximately three-fourths soluble fiber and one-fourth insoluble fiber totaling 35 grams per day. There are many online guides to break down the details and advise how to get fiber. Over-the-counter medication can be helpful to fill the gaps and is available in pill or powder forms.

### 5. <u>Nutrients—Healthy Carbohydrates, Healthy Proteins, Smart Fats, One Treat</u>

A basic guideline is to consider how many portions from each type of energy source you include in your daily diet. These are carbohydrates, proteins, and fats. A carbohydrate that raises blood sugar rapidly is classified as being high glycemic index—or very similar to the effect of sugar. This type of carb is considered a treat. A complex carb describes carbohydrates that have color: whole wheat bread, sweet potato, brown rice, oatmeal or quinoa. A healthy protein is lean meat, fish, eggs, nuts, low fat cheese or legumes. And, healthy fats include nuts, avocado, olive oil, and egg yolks. A simplified guideline for a daily healthy diet is to eat five portions each of healthy carbs and proteins, three servings of healthy fats, and allow for one treat of sugar or high glycemic carbohydrate each day. Green vegetables can be consumed freely without counting.

## 6. <u>Activity—5,000 steps for weight maintenance; 10,000 steps for weight loss</u>

A healthy exercise plan includes heart-raising aerobic exercise, strength training, and stretching. There are many guidebooks and on-line videos and DVDs that can steer you in the right direction. Because it has helped me and many of my patients, I recommend the book *Body for Life for Women*. In addition, I encourage practicing at least basic yoga. It is relaxing, not strenuous, perfect for basic stretching and can be used as a meditative practice. If you are looking for a deeper stretching routine and some strength training, I encourage you to practice more strenuous yoga. My favorite yoga program is by Baron Baptiste, and his DVDs can be found on sites such as Amazon.

## 7. <u>Mind-Body Connection—One 5 minute instance each day of metered breathing and gratitude</u>

Every woman will make this practice her own, but the general concept is to find a time and space for complete quiet where she can become aware of her body and breathe. I feel this is different from prayer, because prayer is more an act of interaction, while metered breathing is a time to be in the body as a temple or place of self. Gratitude is very effective to get us out of flight or fight mode, prepare for public speaking or a talk with the boss, and improve focus and memory. Metered breathing can also help you return to sleep in your bed in the middle of the night, but it is best done in a quiet place out of bed before returning to go to sleep.

## Seven Essential Elements for Daily Success

| SEEDS® | Current Habits | Goal Habits | Gap Between Current & Goal Habits |
|---|---|---|---|
| **Water/Fluids**<br>• water servings (oz)<br>• #caffeine servings (oz)<br>• #alcohol servings (oz) | | 80 oz. | |
| **Sleep** | | 50 hours per week | |
| **Vitamins** | | Multivitamin: 1/day<br><br>Vitamin D: 2000 IU<br><br>B Complex: yes | Multivitamin:<br><br>Vitamin D:<br><br>B Complex: |
| **Fiber** | | 35 mg per day or 1 supplement & 5 fruits or vegetables | |
| **Nutrients** | Smart Carbs:<br><br>Smart Proteins:<br><br>Smart Fats: | Smart Carbs: 5 servings<br><br>Smart Proteins: 5 servings<br><br>Smart Fats: 3 servings | Smart Carbs:<br><br>Smart Proteins:<br><br>Smart Fats: |

| SEEDS® | Current Habits | Goal Habits | Gap Between Current & Goal Habits |
|---|---|---|---|
| **Activity** | Aerobic:<br><br>Strength Training:<br><br>Stretching: | Aerobic: 2-3 x per week<br><br>Strength Training: 2-3x per week<br><br>Stretching: 7 x per week | Aerobic:<br><br>Strength Training:<br><br>Stretching: |
| **Mind/Body (MB) Connection**<br>• **Metered Breathing**<br>• **3 Gratitudes** | MB:<br><br>Gratitudes: | 5 minutes twice a day<br><br>3 gratitudes at least once | MB:<br><br>Gratitudes: |

In reviewing the gap between the Current Habits & Goal Habits column in the above chart, what are your barriers?

_____

_____

_____

_____

_____

What is your plan to hit your goal in each category?

_____

_____

_____

_____

# Chapter Seven

## *Tracking My Symptoms with the Menopause Transition Scale™ (MTS)*

The symptoms of menopause will not be mysterious once you understand why they occur. Once you start understanding your triggers and track your symptoms, you will be able to understand which treatment options are best. Whether or not you choose to use estrogen or other prescription medicine to treat your symptoms, triggers can be overwhelming to induce a night sweat. By understanding it is not all about estrogen, you can better self-manage. The Menopause Transition Scale™ (MTS) is a tool to track midlife and menopause symptoms.

The MTS was developed with my patients using plain descriptions of the quantity or degree of bother the symptoms cause. In the pilot study, the MTS became an easy way to track symptoms between visits.

Read each description below and determine what best describes your experience in the last two weeks.

| Symptom | 3 - Easy | 2 - Moderate | 1 - Hard |
|---|---|---|---|
| Hot flashes Night sweats | Rare, predictable | Moderate, predictable | Frequent, unpredictable |
| Libido | Both partners initiate, connected, playful | Minimal initiation, mismatch of desire between partners, relationship okay | Rare to no sex, low desire has affected relationship, strained |
| Weight | Stable, healthy or overweight and losing | Overweight, not losing | Obese or gaining |
| Energy | Good, awaken refreshed | Mostly rested, good and bad days | Mostly tired, poor function |

Diana L. Bitner, MD, NCMP

| Symptom | 3 - Easy | 2 - Moderate | 1 - Hard |
|---|---|---|---|
| Moods | Good, minor cyclical or variations, predictable | Cyclical or new onset with menopause, others notice, some dysfunction | Mostly depressed or anxious, poor function |
| Vaginal dryness/ | Minor vaginal dryness | Cyclical dryness or new onset with menopause | Daily dryness or Dyspareunia (pain with penetration) |
| Bladder complaints | Rare urgency | Some leaking, daily urgency | Daily urgency and/or leaking affecting life habits. |
| Vaginal bleeding | Cyclical, light, or not bleeding | Moderately heavy, predictable, mild pain | Heavy, interfering, unpredictable, significant pain |

Fill in your corresponding answers below.

Hot Flashes/night sweats: _____

Libido: _____

Weight: _____

Energy: _____

Moods: _____

Vaginal dryness/Bladder complaints: _____

Vaginal bleeding: _____

MTS score: _____/21

# Chapter Eight

## *Treating Symptoms with Modern Knowledge*

Every one of us deserves treatment options that are safe and personalized. There are many options to treat our midlife and menopause symptoms. A healthy lifestyle is the foundation for all treatments; all other treatment options work best in conjunction with hydration, sleep, exercise, good food choices, vitamins, fiber, gratitude, and meditation (SEEDS®). There have been many studies to understand which treatments are most effective, and this chapter includes those that have scientific merit. Some are more effective than others. FDA-approved estrogen treatment, with or without progesterone, is the most effective treatment for menopause symptoms. I believe every woman deserves to know her options to feel her best—with or without estrogen. An app is available from the North American Menopause Society (NAMS) called *MenoPro* to help with the decision-making process. The table on the next page is a place to get started.

On the left side of the table are treatment options, and across the top are symptoms that can be helped by these medications. Use the table to think about options and to come up with questions for your doctor, nurse practitioner, physician assistant, or certified nurse midwife to discuss possible prescription options. I recommend you search out a certified menopause practitioner through the North American Menopause Society (menopause.org) website. Menopause practitioners are certified to know which prescription options would be safe and most helpful for you, as well as lifestyle options most likely to be effective.

| SYMPTOMS<br><br>TREATMENT OPTIONS (below) | Hot Flash | Weight Gain | Energy | Libido | Mood | Vaginal Dryness | Urinary Symptom | Vaginal Bleeding |
|---|---|---|---|---|---|---|---|---|
| SEEDS® | x | x | x | x | x | | | |
| Vaginal estrogen: tablet, insert, ring, cream | | | | | | x | x | |
| Vaginal DHEA | | | | | | x | | |
| Vaginal/ vestibule CO2 laser | | | | | | x | | |
| Estrogen alone (only if hysterectomy) | x | | | x | x (off label) | x | x | |
| Estrogen and Progesterone | x | | | x | X (off label) | x | x | |
| Testosterone | | | x | x | | x | | |
| Progesterone IUD | | | | | | | | x |
| Oral Progesterone | | | | | | | | x |
| SSRI | x (off-label) | | | | x | | | |
| SNRI | x (off label) | | | | x | | | |

| SYMPTOMS / TREATMENT OPTIONS (below) | Hot Flash | Weight Gain | Energy | Libido | Mood | Vaginal Dryness | Urinary Symptom | Vaginal Bleeding |
|---|---|---|---|---|---|---|---|---|
| Anti-anxiety Rx (other class) | x (off label) | | | | x | | | |
| Soy (Equol) supplement | x | | | | | | | |
| Clinical behaviorial therapy | x | | | x | x | | | |
| Clinical hypnosis | x | x | | | x | | | |
| Acupuncture | x | | | | | | | |

The foundation for treating midlife and menopause symptoms is a healthy lifestyle. In addition, the more of the SEEDS® you are able to incorporate into your everyday life, the better you will age and the better you will feel. When women get in the habit of incorporating SEEDS® into their daily lifestyle—with or without hormone medication—everything is better. If hormone medicine is not safe for you, there are many other prescription options (such as SSRI or SNRI medication) for treatment of hot flashes. Local vaginal estrogen is safe and acts in the vagina, and could even be an option for women who have had breast or other estrogen-receptor positive cancers.

If you are a good candidate for Hormone Replacement Therapy (HRT), here are several reasons to consider estrogen and/or progesterone hormone medication therapy:

FDA-approved reasons:

• Improve moderate to severe hot flashes/night sweats

- Decrease vaginal dryness

- Help prevent osteoporosis

- Use of progesterone for protection of the uterus lining

Off-label uses: (meaning not FDA-approved reasons, but acceptable and standard of care among certified menopause practitioners)

- Improve sleep

- Stabilize mood and improve changes

- Possibly improve sexual desire

- Possibly improve sexual arousal

- Possibly improve your ability to have an orgasm

Here are some reasons it might not be safe to take systemic estrogen or progesterone and to seek professional advice from a certified menopause specialist and other specialist as indicated:

- History of deep venous blood clots in leg or lung

- Genetic (or family history-based) risk for deep blood clots in leg or lung

- Personal history of breast cancer or other estrogen or progesterone-positive cancer

- Prior heart attack, active heart disease (i.e., plaque) or very high risk for heart attack

- Prior stroke, significant blockage in carotid, or other high risk for stroke

- More than ten years from your last menstrual period

- Presence of metabolic syndrome

Options of how to take systemic (in the blood) (I) <u>estrogen</u> (II) <u>progesterone</u>:

|  I  |  II  |
|-----|------|
| Pill—conjugated | Oral pill—synthetic |
| Pill—bio-equivalent | Oral pill—bio-equivalent |
| Patch | IUD—synthetic but low systemic exposure |
| Spray | Patch—synthetic |
| Lotion | Vaginal gel—bio-equivalent |

How to use: cyclical during perimenopause and continuous after menopause begins

MTS: ____/21

Last menstrual period: _____

| | | |
|---|---|---|
| Hysterectomy | Y | N |
| Removal of both (or second) ovary | Y | N |

Past medical history:

| | | |
|---|---|---|
| Migraines with blindness | Y | N |
| High cholesterol:  LDL | Y | N |
| Triglycerides | Y | N |
| Stroke | Y | N |
| Heart attack | Y | N |
| High blood sugar (fasting >100 _____    A1C >6.2 _____) | Y | N |
| Waist circumference >35in. | Y | N |
| Diabetes | Y | N |
| Osteoporosis | Y | N |
| Cancer | Y | N |

If yes, type of cancer: _____

If yes, Estrogen-Receptor positive?         Y   N

Surgeries:

    Removal of one ovary         Y   N

    Removal of both ovaries         Y   N

    Removal of uterus         Y   N

    Removal of cervix         Y   N

Breast biopsy:         Y   N

    Benign         Y   N

    Malignant         Y   N

Last Mammogram:

    BIRADS Category _____

    Density Classification _____

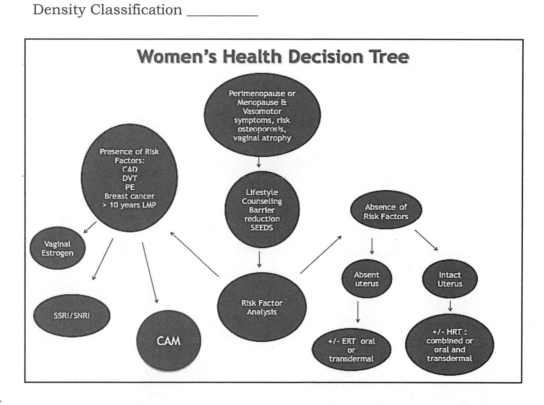

Options I might consider:

_____

_____

_____

_____

Expectations/hopes:

_____

_____

_____

_____

Fears:

_____

_____

_____

_____

Possible side effects of HRT to consider:

_____

_____

_____

_____

Questions?

_____

_____

_____

_____

# Chapter Nine

## *Creating My Life Action Plan*

You've made it this far and have your goals established. To see your goals become reality, a plan is needed. Transform your goals into action and build the momentum by setting up a five-step plan.

- Dream it

- Research it

- Decide action plan

- Determine logistics

- Put it on the calendar to improve likelihood of execution

Journal each of these steps, asking yourself questions about what this will look like for you to achieve your goals. Start a daily journal to record your process and reassess your progress. What works? What doesn't work? What are your barriers and what steps can you take to overcome your barriers?

**My Life Action Plan**

The goal of this chart below is to think about each category of wellness and clearly state your personal POS and PIP. If they are not equal, and you want to achieve your POS, what barriers do you need to overcome and what is your plan to reach your POS? This is a tool to clearly map out your journey.

Diana L. Bitner, MD, NCMP

| Wellness Category | POS | PIP | Risks Identified | Recommendations |
|---|---|---|---|---|
| Ability to be active | | | | |
| Obesity | | | | |
| Cancer | | | | |
| Lung | | | | |
| Colorectal | | | | |

78

| Breast | | | | |
|---|---|---|---|---|
| Diabetes | | | | |
| Ease of Coping | | | | |
| Phase of Ovarian Function | | | | |

| Good Bones | | | | |
|---|---|---|---|---|
| Heart Disease | | | | |
| Income Security | | | | |

# Chapter Ten

# *Healthy Aging in an Unhealthy World*

Successful women do not get where they are by chance or luck. To realize a dream requires determination, hard work and planning. Over the years of being a busy mom and physician, I have learned from my mistakes, and from my patients' and friends' solutions for coping with challenges to a healthy lifestyle. Having a time budget will ensure important things get accomplished. The following table is how I plan my week. I create it on Sunday night and review it frequently all week. The key is to add ourselves to the list and not ignore our own needs.

The SEEDS® is such a good list to organize life around, because it ensures the necessary elements of a healthy lifestyle are being met. Perhaps you are already an expert of organization, and the next pages are too basic for you. It is meant to highlight again that there is no magic pill to bring success; instead it is about having a plan.

As a reminder: SEEDS® = Seven Essential Elements of Daily Success

- **Water**—Eight 10 oz glasses every day

- **Sleep**—50 hours every week

- **Vitamins**—Multivitamin, Vitamin D, Calcium

- **Fiber**—35 grams per day

- **Nutrients**

    A. Healthy Carbohydrates—Approximately 5 servings every day.
    B. Healthy Proteins—Approximately 5 servings every day.
    C. Smart Fats—Approximately 3 servings every day.
    D. One Treat.

- **Activity**—5,000 steps for weight maintenance; 10,000 steps for weight loss.

  A. Aerobic
  B. Strength Training
  C. Stretching

- **Mind-Body Connection**—One 5 minute instance each day of metered breathing and gratitude.

  - Close mouth
  - Open eyes
  - Focus vision on single spot
  - Breathe normally through nose

To demonstrate, I took a typical week for me and how I plan my time.

**EXAMPLE CHECKLIST**

| Weekly Checklist to Complete SEEDS® | Example of Plan |
| --- | --- |
| Menu:<br>• Complex Carbs: 5 per day<br>• Protein: 5 per day<br>• Healthy Fats: 3 per day<br>• Treat: one simple sugar per day | • Breakfast: Ezekiel toast/PB/honey<br>• Snack: 5 whole grain crackers/ 2 cheese sticks<br>• Lunch: Salad, brown rice, leftover chicken<br>• Snack: Apple/10 walnuts<br>• Dinner: Roasted salmon, roasted broccoli, salad (for kids add brown rice)<br>• Snack: None (or 1/2 yellow banana if exercise) |

| Weekly Checklist to Complete SEEDS® | Example of Plan |
|---|---|
| Appointments (self, family members including pets) | • Tuesday @ 1pm: Son dentist appointment<br>• Thursday @ 3pm: Cats' vet appointment |
| Exercise:<br>• Aerobic 3x/week<br>• Strength training 3x/week<br>• Stretching: Yoga 1x per week and 10 minute stretching sequence every day | • Monday @ 8pm: Vinyasa yoga 40 minutes (Youtube)<br>• Tuesday @ 8pm: Spin bike, 30 minute intervals<br>• Wednesday @ 8pm: Spin bike, 45 minutes moderate with intervals<br>• Thursday @ 8pm: Spin bike 15 minutes; upper body weightlifting 20 minutes<br>• Friday: Light stretching only<br>• Saturday: Spin bike, 45 minutes difficult with intervals<br>• Sunday: Swim 40 minutes |
| Quiet time:<br>• 5 minutes twice a day | • AM and PM stretching<br>• Pick an intention word and be still |

| Weekly Checklist to Complete SEEDS® | Example of Plan |
|---|---|
| Fun | • Meet friends Friday evening<br>• Hike with friends Saturday morning |
| Weekly to-do list:<br><br>Categories:<br><br>• Home<br>• Work<br>• Etc. | Home:<br><br>• Pay bills<br>• Call carpet cleaner<br>• Take cats to vet<br>• Kids' schedules<br><br>Work:<br><br>• Projects<br>• Research meetings |

| PLAN | M | T | W | Th | F | Sat | Sun |
|---|---|---|---|---|---|---|---|
| **SEEDS®**<br><br>**Goal vs. done** | Goal 7<br>Done | Goal 7<br>Done | Goal 7<br>Done | Goal 7<br>Done | Goal 7<br>Done | Goal 7<br>Done | Goal 7<br>Done |
| Menu | | | | | | | |
| Appointments (self, family members including pets) | | | | | | | |
| Exercise | | | | | | | |
| Quiet time | | | | | | | |

| PLAN | M | T | W | Th | F | Sat | Sun |
|---|---|---|---|---|---|---|---|
| | | | | | | | |
| Fun | | | | | | | |
| Weekly to-do list: Category: <ul><li>Home</li><li>Work</li><li>Etc</li></ul> | | | | | | | |

# Chapter Eleven

## *A Partner's Guide to Understanding Menopause*

Menopause is a family affair. Changing hormones, as well as the natural aging process, affects not only the woman experiencing the symptoms but also everyone in her life. To be fair, and to build relationships instead of causing more strain, everyone needs to be understood and supported. Healthy relationships are built on trust, mutual support, and each person owning their stuff. "Stuff" includes needs, feelings, and cause behind words and actions. Having a night of poor sleep or feeling cranky about weight gain does not give a woman the right to yell at her partner about leaving his shirt on the floor, and a partner feeling hurt about no sex does not have the right to complain about her working late on an important project.

The challenges of midlife and menopause can be a gift to remember to be honest about personal feelings and needs, and to ask what the other person needs as well. Anyone can be kind, giving and supportive when life is easy, but the true test of a person and relationship is when there are challenges. It is important to start early. For example, in perimenopause when the days before a period lead to bloating, headaches, bad moods and night sweats, it can be an opener to "my body is changing, I do not like this, and I need to figure this out." And the partner could say, "I can tell you do not feel well; how can I help and what is happening?" There are many ways to have the conversation, but coming from a place of love and support, and stating the obvious, is the only way to start. Being authentic and honest helps. If there are resentments, say it! Phrases such as "I feel bad when I do not get to have sex with you," or "I feel loved when we talk," or " I feel loved when you tell me what is going on" is honest and puts the feeling out there. Talk before it is too late and resentment builds up!

What is hard about your current state?

_____

_____

_____

_____

_____

Frustrations? Barriers?

_____

_____

_____

_____

Specific questions or problems?

_____

_____

_____

_____

Fears?

_____

_____

_____

Hopes (for myself, for her)?

_____

_____

_____

_____

Questions for your partner, her doctor, and your doctor?

_____

_____

_____

_____

Once this is complete, you can use this as a guide to a conversation where everything is on the table. Use language such as "I care so much that I want to understand more about us as we change with age and how we can support each other."

Paraphrasing from the book, *Getting the Love you Want,* for relationships to last, it is necessary that each partner gives the other what he/she needs. To get what each partner wants, he/she has to ask for it. Honest communication is crucial and making it safe for each person to be honest is the key. Each partner has to own his/her issues, and the worksheet above can be the best place to start.

# *Final Thoughts from Diana*

At 53, I am just starting to understand my path, and see how everything in my life has added up to who I am and what I have to offer. All the people in my life and my experiences have played a part.

When I get caught up in worry, or drama, or allow doubt to overshadow intuition, my heart and frontal cortex close down, and I say and do things I shouldn't. How do I keep an open heart and thus stay connected to my purpose and my true self? I, for the time being, will close my eyes for a second to smell an open fire and see a cozy scene of good friends, and remember a feeling of calm. After being in that place for a minute or two, I take the situation at hand and do my best to stay true.

I am a woman who is blessed with a life that fits me well. But it did not just happen. My life has been marked by bright moments of love, success and clarity, and also by times of fear, abandonment and uncertainty. I have dreamed of being a doctor since a young age, and I am thankful for inborn focus which has kept me on track. Learning to own my power has been crucial and requires continued daily practice.

I wrote this workbook because I have expertise and insight to share, and I am still sometimes surprised that my approach to patient care works time and time again. For over 25 years, I have been blessed to be included in women's lives at their most important moments. Each woman and her situation is unique, from pregnancies and births, health histories and conditions such as diabetes and cancer, and crises of postpartum depression, to cheating husbands and emergencies like unwanted hysterectomies in women who couldn't have children. I have had to learn to wear many hats, switching between surgeon, psychologist, mother, and friend.

Using the W*A*I*Pointes® principles has made it easier to see how every aspect of a woman's life fits together to make her well or unwell as she ages. A big part of my practice is seeing women for their annual exam. More and more, I have seen how these appointments turn into W*A*I*Pointes® visits.

Wherever you are in your mid-life journey—at the starting line, still walking or running, or already across the menopause finish line—you know your body and your life are changing. Very few of us want, or wish, to age or grow old.

What's the alternative? Short of finding a genie in a bottle, a working time travel machine or that elusive fountain of youth, you can't stop aging, but you can choose how you'll go about it. Choose to age gracefully, age smartly, age with energy, vitality, drive, ambition and happiness, age with a sense of adventure. Use the change of life to change your life. Use it as a ticket to the best time of your life, a catalyst for personal transformation, an opportunity to reenergize your body, mind and soul. And there is no time like the present.

As a physician, I have a unique opportunity to share the journey with my patients, to support them and cheer them on. As a healer, I feel fulfilled when I see a patient jettison bad habits, clear the clutter from her life and embrace daily lifestyle changes that will keep her healthier and happier in the years to come. As a 53-year-old mom and woman who, just like you, is struggling with my own hot flashes and midlife health challenges, I am also a fellow traveler on this midlife journey.

I wrote the *I Want to Age Like That!* book and this corresponding workbook because I couldn't find a book or resource that fully and completely incorporated traditional medicine with a full body, mind and spirit holistic approach that talks about nutrition and phase of ovarian function, that asks women to revisit their goals and to imagine the future they want, to create a picture of self that will turn into a self-fulfilling "prophecy." Frustration was the mother of this invention.

As I've stated throughout, my vision and goal were to help you age healthfully and vibrantly without chronic illness, cancer, or pain by using your dreams and goals as motivation to make good daily choices.

And now that you've figured out your Place in Process (PIP), developed your Picture of Self (POS), created your Life Action Plan and completed the questionnaires, I invite you to venture onto the website (truewomenshealth.com), to delve deeper and discover more tools to help you refine your path to wellness. I invite you to meet new friends as we build a community of women on the verge of changing midlife.

Enjoy the journey,

Dr. Diana L. Bitner, MD, NCMP, FACOG

To learn about our clinical practice

or to order

*I Want to Age Like That!*

visit our website at www.truewomenshealth.com